Tony's Treasure Hunt

Story and pictures by

HOLLY and JOHN PETERSON

SCHOLASTIC BOOK SERVICES

Published by Scholastic Book Services, a division
of Scholastic Magazines, Inc., New York, N.Y.

You may want to read another book by John Peterson.

TULIPS, A Science Story Without Words

Single copy price 35¢. Quantity prices available on request.

Copyright © 1964 by Holly and John Peterson. All rights reserved.

2nd printing . . . . December 1965

Printed in the U.S.A.

To Chris, a treasure hunter of our acquaintance

One day Tony and his cat, Growler, found a mysterious box.

Tony tried to open the box.
He hit it against a rock.

And he said some magic words.

But the box would not open.

"Meow," said Growler.

Tony looked at Growler.

The cat was wearing a key!

"Growler!" said Tony. "Where did you get that key?"

Growler just said, "Meow!"

So Tony took the key. Maybe...
maybe it would open the box.

It did!

And Tony found a note inside...

For until the you mystery come at treasure last follow to your the nose garden hose.

Tony could read the note. But he could not understand it.

Then he read just the words with a line under them:

<u>For</u> <u>the</u> <u>mystery</u> <u>treasure</u>,

<u>follow</u> <u>your</u> <u>nose</u>

Next he read the words that had no lines under them:

until you come at last

to the garden hose.

"Come on, Growler!" cried Tony.
"Let's find the garden hose."

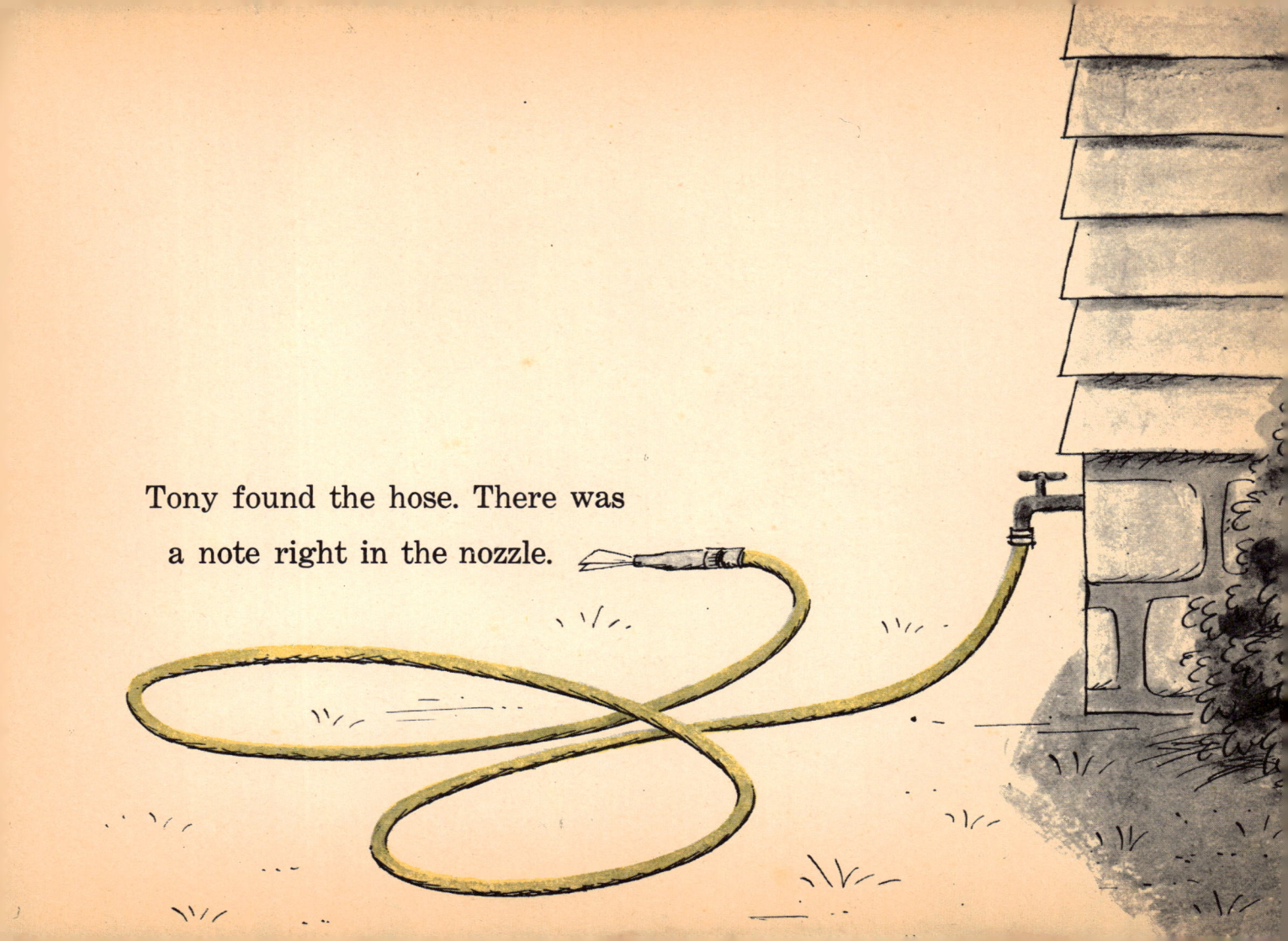

Tony found the hose. There was a note right in the nozzle.

Find something shiny
Then you will know
That is the way
That you must go

Tony read the note.

Tony looked around for something shiny.

He saw Growler's shiny eyes.

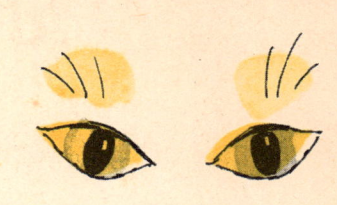

He saw the shiny car.

He saw a shiny yellow pail.

But not one of the shiny things helped him.

"Aw rats!" said Tony. "We will never find the treasure."

Tony was so angry, he kicked the ground.
A shiny new penny hopped into the air.
"That's it!" cried Tony. "Pennies are shiny!"

14

"Look! — more pennies," said Tony.
Tony and Growler followed the trail
of shiny new pennies. The trail led them to . . .

. . . a big rock.

Tony found this note under the rock:

If you read this message you will see the next clue lies in a big old ---

The words made the shape of a pine tree!
Tony and Growler ran to the pine tree in the back yard.
They found the next note in the tree.

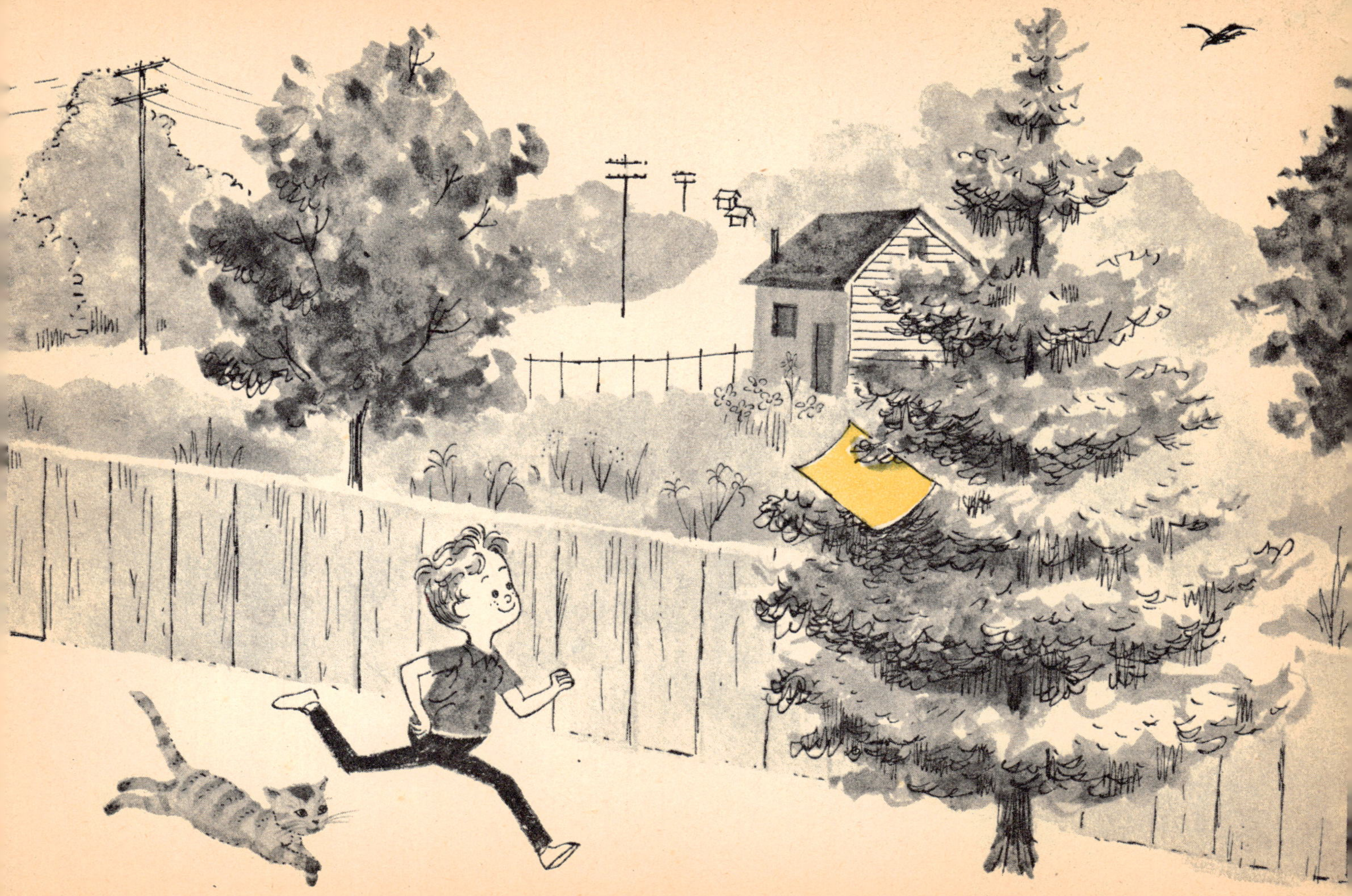

Tony put out his hand for the note—

Just then a big, black crow zoomed down.

He took the note and flew away.

Growler hissed.

Tony shouted, "Come back, you old bird!"

The crow was so frightened, he dropped the note.

Tony picked up the note and read it...

You have looked in trees and lifted up ocks-ray
The next secret clue is in a silver ox-bay

Tony did not understand the two funny words.
Ocks-ray? Ox-bay? He read the note again.
"You have looked in trees and lifted up —"

"Rocks!" shouted Tony.
"Then ox-bay must be box."

"Now where can I find a silver box?" said Tony.
Just then a butterfly flew by.

Growler ran after the butterfly.
Tony ran after Growler.

"Growler, come back!" Tony shouted.

"We have to find a silver box."

Just then the butterfly landed on...

.... the mailbox!

The mailbox was shining like silver in the sun.

"This must be the silver box," said Tony.

There were two notes in the mailbox.

The first note said:

Go to the attic of the old brown 8-15-21-19-5
Look for the hole of a little brown 13-15-21-19-5

The second note looked like this:

a b c d e f g h i j k l m n o
1 2 3 4 5 6 7 8 9 10 11 12 13 14 15

p q r s t u v w x y z
16 17 18 19 20 21 22 23 24 25 26

"Hey! the numbers make words," said Tony.

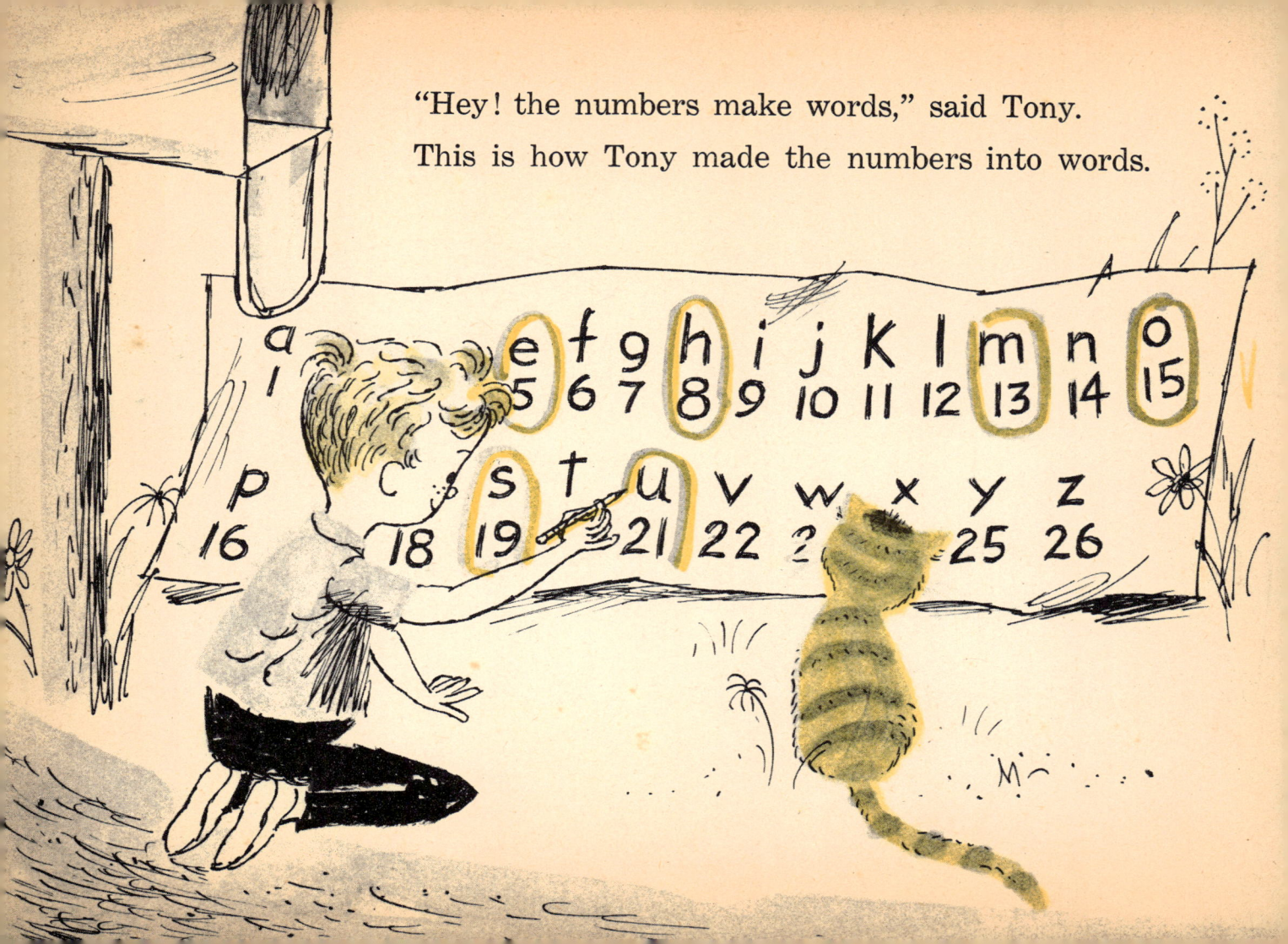

This is how Tony made the numbers into words.

Now he could read the message.

Go to the attic of the old brown 8-15-21-19-5
house

Look for the hole of a little brown 13-15-21-19-5
mouse

"Old brown house," said Tony.

"Hey! *I* live in the old brown house!"

"Slam!" went the front door.

"Clop, clop, clop," went Tony's feet as he ran upstairs.

"Meow," said Growler.

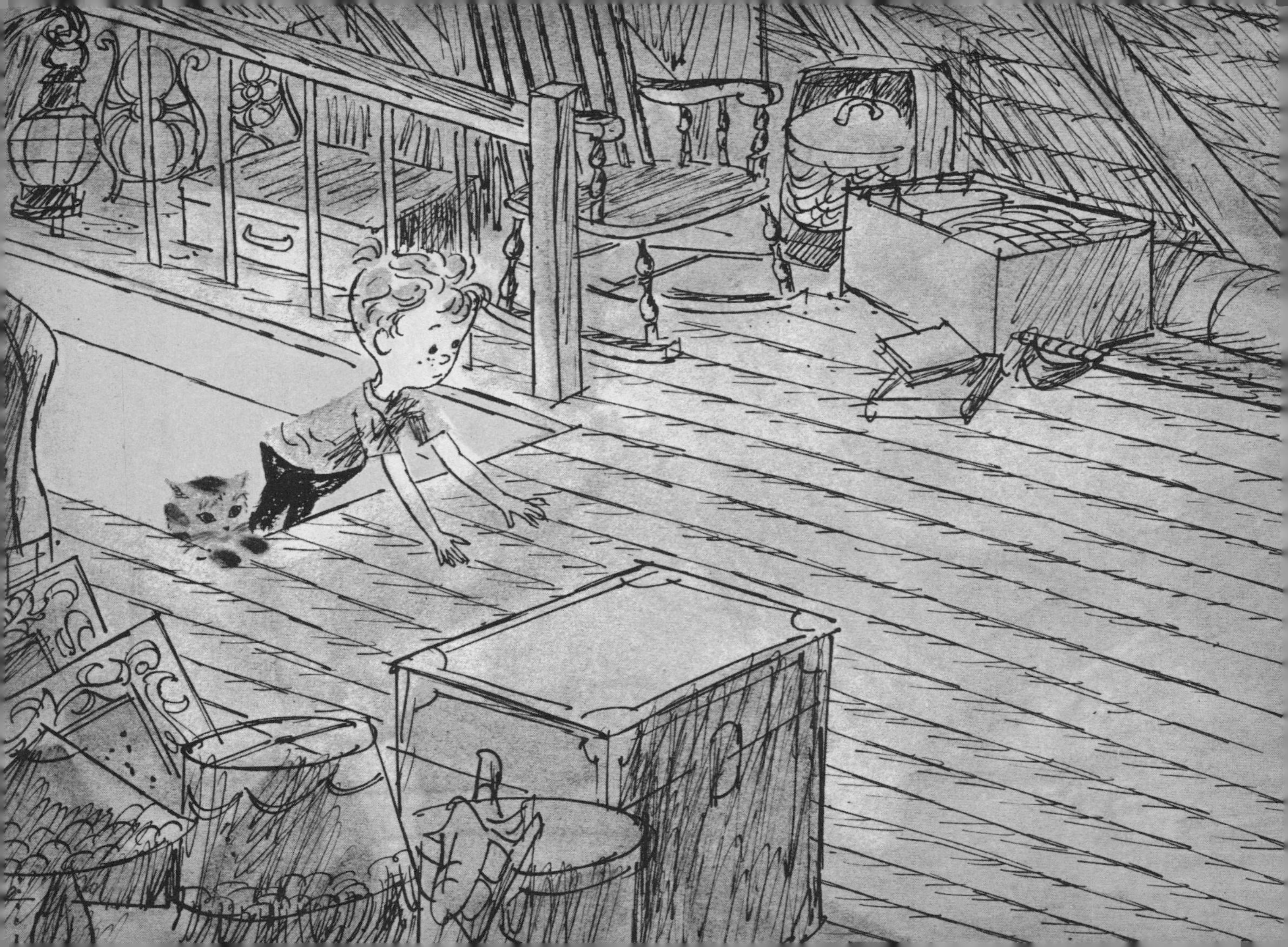

Tony and Growler came to the attic.
And there was the last note... in the mouse hole.

Tony read the message:

You had a silver key
And you opened up a lock,

Peeked in a garden hose,
Followed pennies to a rock,

Found a silver mailbox
At the front of the house,

And this note—the last one—
In a hole for a mouse.

But where is the treasure?
This note tells you where.

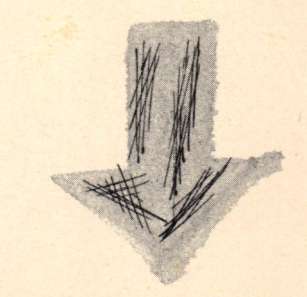

Go to the dining room.
The treasure is there.

Tony knew how to read this message!
He held it up to the mirror.

"Hooray!" said Tony. He ran downstairs.
Growler was right behind him.

They ran into the dining room.

"Surprise!" said his mother.
"Surprise!" said his father.

"Happy Birthday!" shouted his friends.

"Look on the table, Tony," said his father.

And there Tony saw — on the dining-room table — a birthday cake and birthday presents.

"Oh boy! This is the best treasure we ever found, isn't it, Growler?" said Tony.

"*Me-ow!*" said Growler.